TV Trivia
Quiz Book

Tommy Jenkins

**BARNES
&NOBLE
BOOKS**
NEW YORK

The author wishes to thank all those who provided questions, expertise, and/or encouragement: Tom Jenkins, Cheryl Jenkins, Dana Goodman, Sharon Bosley, Mike Ferrari, Heather Russell-Revesz, Rick Campbell, Stuart Miller, and Sallye Leventhal.

ISBN 0-7607-2669-8

Book design by Lundquist Design, New York

Printed and bound in the United States of America

01 02 03 MP 9 8 7 6 5 4 3 2 1

OPM

Q: How long was *The Garry Moore Show* on the air? What was the name of its announcer?

Q: What TV comedy star got her start on Garry Moore's show?

Q: Who was the moderator on *I've Got a Secret* from 1952 to 1964?

Q: What popular musical variety show featured the Lennon Sisters? What were their first names?

Q: How long was this musical variety show on the air?

Q: Who was the star of *Dragnet*? What character did he play?

A: *The Garry Moore Show* was on CBS from 1958 to 1964, then returned in 1966 for a season. It starred Garry Moore, with Durward Kirby as the announcer.

A: The show introduced Carol Burnett, who went on to have her own show (1967–1979) on CBS.

A: Garry Moore.

A: Dianne, Janet, Kathy, and Peggy were the Lennon Sisters on the *Lawrence Welk Show.*

A: Beginning in 1955, Lawrence Welk's show was on ABC for sixteen years, and syndicated for another eleven years. It's still on the air! The repeats of the old shows are being shown in syndication and on PBS.

A: Jack Webb played Sergeant Joe Friday.

Q: Boss Hogg's restaurant/bar was one of the central locations on *The Dukes of Hazzard*. What was the name of this establishment?

Q: Bo and Luke Duke were two of the most popular characters on television in the early 1980s. Name the actors who played Bo and Luke.

Q: Who sang the theme song and also served as the narrator on *The Dukes of Hazzard*?

Q: Denver Pyle played Uncle Jesse on the *Dukes of Hazzard*. On what other show did he have a recurring role as the head of the Darling family?

Q: When was the first episode of *Laverne & Shirley* televised?

A: The Boar's Nest.

A: Bo was played by John Schneider and Luke was played by Tom Wopat.

A: Waylon Jennings.

A: Denver Pyle appeared in several episodes of *The Andy Griffith Show*.

A: January 27, 1976, marked the debut of the show, starring Penny Marshall as Laverne DeFazio and Cindy Williams as Shirley Feeney. The show ran until 1983.

Q: On *Laverne & Shirley*, Laverne had a very peculiar diet. What was her favorite drink?

Q: Sticking with *Laverne & Shirley*, Shirley had a cherished stuffed toy cat. What was its name?

Q: Who was the title character of the 1963–1966 television series *My Favorite Martian*?

Q: When was the first episode of *I Love Lucy* shown?

Q: What was the name of the club Ricky Ricardo owned on *I Love Lucy*?

Q: What was Lucy's maiden name?

A: Milk and Pepsi mixed together.

A: Boo Boo Kitty.

A: Ray Walston played the Martian who, disguised as Uncle Martin, lived with Timothy O'Hara (Bill Bixby).

A: On October 15, 1951, CBS broadcast the first Lucy show. The episode was entitled "The Girls Want to Go to a Nightclub." The original show ran from 1951 to 1957.

A: The Ricky Ricardo Babalu Club. He originally worked at the Tropicana.

A: MacGillicuddy.

Q: Lucy managed to blow a shot at acting in a commercial by getting drunk on the product she was supposed to endorse. What was the name of the product?

Q: The family on the 1970s sitcom *The Brady Bunch* was too good to be true. What did Mike Brady do for a living to support his ideal family?

Q: The Brady boys were lucky enough to get visits from several famous athletes. What famous pitcher made a guest appearance? What NFL quarterback gave Bobby Brady a few pointers?

Q: Athletes as guest stars has been a TV staple for years. What Major League manager showed up on *The Beverly Hillbillies* to scout Jethro?

A: Vitameatavegemin.

A: Mike Brady (Robert Reed), was an architect.

A: Pitcher Don Drysdale. Joe Namath was the NFL quarterback.

A: Leo Durocher made a guest appearance on this 1960s series.

Q: What did the Beverly Hillbillies call their swimming pool?

Q: On the 1980s drama *Magnum P.I.*, Magnum lived on an extravagant estate in Hawaii. Name the owner of the estate.

Q: The caretaker of the estate continuously caused Magnum problems. What was the name of the caretaker?

Q: What real-life couple met and fell in love as the stars of *Bridget Loves Bernie*?

Q: On *Family Ties*, what was the single biggest problem that Steven and Elyse Keaton (played by Michael Gross and Meredith Baxter) had with their teenage son Alex?

A: The cement pond.

A: Robin Masters, (voiced by Orson Welles), who was never seen on the show. The mustachioed Tom Selleck became a 1980s heartthrob playing the title character.

A: Jonathan Higgins, played by John Hillerman.

A: Meredith Baxter became Meredith Baxter Birney after she fell in love with actor David Birney while they were playing Bridget and Bernie Steinberg on this 1972–1973 sitcom. The marriage lasted longer than the show, but, like the show, the marriage didn't last forever.

A: Alex (Michael J. Fox) was a Republican. Elyse and Steven, his parents, were not. *Family Ties* aired from 1982 to 1989.

Q: What Oscar winning actor made a guest appearance playing Michael J. Fox's uncle on *Family Ties*?

Q: Match the catch phrase on the left with the show it is from on the right:
1. Book 'em Dano.   A. *Dragnet*
2. You big dummy.   B. *Sanford and Son*
3. Just the facts.   C. *The Simpsons*
4. D'oh!   D. *Hawaii Five O*

Q: In what year did *The Beverly Hillbillies* first rumble into Hollywood, California?

Q: One of the biggest questions of the early 1980s was "Who Shot J. R.?" So, who did shoot J. R.?

Q: What was the name of J. R.'s ranch?

A: Tom Hanks.

A: 1. D; 2. B; 3. A; 4. C

A: *The Beverly Hillbillies*, which starred Buddy Ebsen as the *nouveau riche* oil tycoon Jed Clampett, was first broadcast in 1962.

A: *Dallas*'s scheming J. R. Ewing, played by Larry Hagman, was shot by his sister-in-law Kristin, played by Mary Crosby. Apparently Kristin was driven to a murderous rage when J. R. refused to marry her, like he had promised.

A: South Fork.

Q: On the long running series *Bonanza*
(1959–1973) there were three Cartwright boys.
Name the characters and the actors who played
them.

Q: What was the name of the Cartwright's cook on
Bonanza?

Q: What was the name of the Cartwright's ranch
on *Bonanza*?

Q: Who played Commander Adama on the late
1970s sci-fi series *Battlestar Galactica*?

Q: Tim Taylor's neighbor on *Home Improvement*
(1991–1999) was always there when he needed
advice. What was the neighbor's name?

A: Pernell Roberts played Adam, Dan Blocker played Hoss, and Michael Landon played Little Joe.

A: Hop Sing, played by Victor Sen Yung.

A: The Ponderosa.

A: Lorne Greene, who also starred as the father of the Cartwright boys on *Bonanza*.

A: Wilson.

Q: Tim Allen's character, Tim Taylor, had a home improvement televison show, hence the title of the series. But what was the name of the show within a show?

Q: Who provided the voice for the mysterious Charlie on *Charlie's Angels* (1976–1981)?

Q: In the original series, what actresses played the angels of Charlie?

Q: Who was the lead in the *Six Million Dollar Man* (1974–1978)?

Q: For a short time on *Friends*, Ross had a pet monkey. What was the name of the monkey? What was the name of the movie the monkey ended up appearing in?

A: *Tool Time*, sponsored by Binford Tools.

A: John Forsythe.

A: Kate Jackson, Farrah Fawcett, and Jaclyn Smith made up the original lineup. Cheryl Ladd, Shelley Hack, and Tanya Roberts were later replacements.

A: Lee Majors (then married to Farrah Fawcett) played Colonel Steve Austin, the test pilot who had the expensive replacement implants.

A: Marcel was the monkey who appeared in the fictional *Outbreak 2. Friends* debuted in 1994.

Q: How many times has Ross been married on *Friends*? Who was he married to?

Q: Joey on *Friends* got a big break in his career when he was cast on a soap opera. What soap was he on? What tragic accident caused the death of his soap opera character?

Q: Psychologist Dr. Joyce Brothers won the big prize on *The $64,000 Question*. In what subject did she compete?

Q: Buffy lives in a pretty strange town on *Buffy the Vampire Slayer*. What is the name of this cursed place?

Q: *Maude* and *The Jeffersons* both share the distinction of being spinoffs from the same show. What show?

A: He's been married three times. His first wife, with whom he has a son, was Carol. His second wife was Emily, and his third wife was Rachel. Ross and Rachel got married one drunken night in Las Vegas.

A: *Days of Our Lives*. After being insulted by Joey, the writers on *Days of Our Lives* had his character, Dr. Drake Ramore, fall down an elevator shaft.

A: Dr. Joyce Brothers's expertise was in boxing.

A: The name of Buffy's home town is Sunnydale.

A: *All in the Family*, which ran from 1971–1979.

Q: What kind of car "ran great" in the theme song to *All in the Family*?

Q: Another *All in the Family* question: What was Meathead's full name?

Q: What business was George Jefferson in that enabled him to "move on up"?

Q: On *Cheers* (1982–1993), Norm's wife was often referred to but never fully seen. What was her name?

Q: What was Sam Malone's job before he owned the bar?

A: A (Buick) Lasalle.

A: Michael Stivic, played by Rob Reiner.

A: On the sitcom *The Jeffersons* (1975–1985), George owned several dry cleaning stores.

A: Vera.

A: Sam Malone, played by Ted Danson, was a pitcher for the Boston Red Sox.

Q: The money conscious Rebecca on *Cheers* ended up falling in love with a plumber. Who played the plumber?

Q: Barney Miller worked at a police precinct full of funny characters. What precinct was it?

Q: On the detective series *Baretta* (1975–1978), the title character had a pet bird. What was his bird's name?

Q: Who sang the theme song to *Baretta*?

Q: *The A-Team* was a quintessential 1980s action show. What were the character names of the four men who comprised the A-Team?

A: Tom Berenger.

A: The 12th Precinct, New York City. *Barney Miller* aired from 1975–1982.

A: The cockatoo was named Fred. Tony Baretta was played by Robert Blake.

A: Sammy Davis, Jr. sang "Keep Your Eye on the Sparrow."

A: Hannibal, Face, Murdock, and B. A. Barracus.

Q: Mr. T played the tough B. A. Barracus on *The A-Team*. But B. A. had one great fear that always gave the team problems. What was his fear?

Q: *The Honeymooners* (1952–1957) centered around Jackie Gleason's Ralph Kramden. What did Ralph do for a living?

Q: Where did Ed Norton (Art Carney) work?

Q: Where did Ralph, Alice, Ed, and Trixie live?

Q: Jack, Chrissy, and Janet were the three main characters on *Three's Company*. What was the name of their womanizing neighbor?

A: He was afraid to fly.

A: He was a bus driver.

A: Norton worked in the sewers.

A: In an apartment building on Chauncey Street, in the Bensonhurst section of Brooklyn.

A: Larry.

Q: On *Three's Company*, what was the name of the bar where the regulars hung out?

Q: On the series *Frasier*, Martin (Frasier's father), has a cute little dog that annoys the heck out of Frasier. What is the dog's name? What breed is Martin's dog?

Q: What was the name of the nosy reporter on *The Incredible Hulk* (1978–1982)? In the opening credits he was warned to not make the Hulk angry.

Q: What Oscar winning actress played Roseanne's grandmother on *Roseanne* (1988–1997)?

Q: What was the name of the nosy super on *One Day At A Time* (1975–1984)?

A: The Regal Beagle.

A: Eddie is a Jack Russell Terrier.

A: Mr. McGee. "Mr. McGee, don't make me angry. You wouldn't like me when I'm angry."

A: Shelley Winters.

A: Dwayne Schneider, played by Pat Harrington, Jr.

Q: What was the name of the intimidating bailiff on *Night Court*?

Q: Name the actor who played a surgeon on *M*A*S*H* and had a guest stint as a doctor on *E.R.*

Q: What "Brat Packer" was originally on *The Facts of Life* (1979–1988)?

Q: On *Felicity*, the title character moved to New York to go to college. Where was she originally from?

Q: On the 1990s show *Beverly Hills 90210*, the kids hung out at a local diner. What was the name of the diner?

A: Bull, played by Richard Moll on the series that ran from 1984–1992.

A: Alan Alda.

A: Molly Ringwald.

A: Palo Alto, California.

A: The Peach Pit.

Q: Whose answering machine on *90210* had the outgoing message, "You know the drill"?

Q: Ally McBeal's former roommate, played by Lisa Nicole Carson, has a recurring role on another popular series. Name the other series.

Q: On *Welcome Back Kotter* (1975–1979), Mr. Kotter taught a group of troubled teens, who were known by what name?

Q: *Welcome Back Kotter* took place in what part of New York?

Q: What was the name of the suburban town where Dick Van Dyke and Mary Tyler Moore lived on the 1960s *The Dick Van Dyke Show*?

A: Dylan McKay, played by Luke Perry.

A: *E.R.* She plays the mother of Dr. Benton's son.

A: The Sweathogs. Mega-star John Travolta started his career as Sweathog Vinnie Barbarino.

A: Brooklyn.

A: New Rochelle, New York.

Q: What was the name of the show where Dick Van Dyke's character worked?

Q: An early break for Tom Hanks came on a sitcom where he had to dress up as a woman. Name the show.

Q: Ralph Mouth was the guy who always had a quick joke on *Happy Days* (1978–1984). But what buttoned-down job did Ralph's father have?

Q: On *Happy Days*, all the kids went to one specific place to make out. What was the name of this lover's paradise?

Q: What was the name of Richie Cunningham's long time girlfriend whom he eventually married?

A: *The Alan Brady Show.* Alan Brady was played by Carl Reiner.

A: *Bosom Buddies.* Tom dressed in heels and a wig from 1980–1984.

A: Optometrist.

A: Inspiration Point.

A: Lorrie Beth.

Q: What was The Fonz's full name?

Q: Name the actor who played Arnold on *Happy Days*. What popular 1984 movie did he later appear in?

Q: Al (played by Al Molinaro) took over running the restaurant Arnold's on *Happy Days*. On what earlier sitcom did this actor appear as a recurring character? Hint: he played a cop.

Q: Willona on *Good Times* (1974–1979) was always quick with a comeback. She later showed her softer side when she adopted a troubled girl. What was the girl's name and what actress played her?

A: Arthur Fonzarelli.

A: Pat Morita played Arnold. He later starred in the
Karate Kid.

A: Al Molinaro played the cop Murray Greshler on *The
Odd Couple* (1970–1975).

A: Janet Jackson played the troubled Penny on *Good
Times*. Willona was played by Ja'net DuBois.

Q: Name the actress who played Willis's girlfriend on *Different Strokes*. What was the character's name?

Q: Through circumstances typically convoluted, George Constanza on *Seinfeld* once needed to replace a loaf of bread. To help George, Jerry steals a loaf from an old woman on the street. What kind of bread caused all this trouble?

Q: After burning down his fiancée's parent's cabin, George learns that her father had an affair with a famous writer. Who was the writer?

Q: George's fiancée died before their wedding took place. How did she die?

Q: What was the name of Jerry's uncle on *Seinfeld*?

A: Janet Jackson played Willis's girlfriend, Charlotte, on the series that ran from 1978–1986.

A: Marble rye.

A: John Cheever.

A: Susan died from poisoning after licking the cheap envelopes that George bought to mail the wedding invitations.

A: Uncle Leo.

Q: *Seinfeld* again: What book did Jerry have checked out of the New York Public Library since high school?

Q: Who worked for Vandelay Industries on *Seinfeld*?

Q: Of the following famous comedy writers, which one did *not* write for Sid Caesar's *Your Show of Shows* (1950–1954)?
A. Woody Allen
B. Neil Simon
C. Norman Lear
D. Larry Gelbart
E. Mel Brooks

A: *The Tropic of Cancer.*

A: Nobody. This was the sham company where George told the unemployment office he was close to getting a job.

A: C. Norman Lear.

Q: Homer Simpson is not the smartest character in the TV universe (or any universe for that matter). On one episode the cause of Homer's intellectual problems is revealed. What is Homer's problem?

Q: What's the name of the "slack-jawed yokel" on *The Simpsons*?

Q: Bart Simpson has had a lot of trouble with one particular "criminal genius," who vowed to kill Bart. Who is this criminal mastermind?

A: He has a crayon stuck in his brain.

A: Cletis.

A: Side-Show Bob, voiced by Kelsey Grammer of *Fraiser*.

Q: Homer Simpson has had quite an eclectic professional life. Which of the following jobs has Homer not tried?
A. Manager for a country singer.
B. Boxer
C. Singer in a barber shop quartet
D. Sanitation commissioner
E. Food critic
F. Race car driver

Q: What was the name of the Grammy winning song Homer Simpson wrote on the episode entitled "Homer's Barbershop Quartet"?

Q: What was the name of the doomed boat on *Gilligan's Island* (1964–1967)?

Q: How long was the original tour supposed to be for the passengers on this boat?

A: F. Race car driver.

A: "Baby on Board."

A: The *S.S. Minnow*.

A: 3 hours.

Q: Match the *Batman* (1966–1968) villain with the actor who played him or her.

1. Egghead   A. Caesar Romero
2. The Riddler   B. Vincent Price
3. The Joker   C. Frank Gorshin
4. The Penguin   D. Burgess Meredith

Q: On the series *Alice*, the title character was an aspiring singer, but had a day job as a waitress. Where did she work?

Q: Rick Shroeder played a cop on *NYPD Blue*. What was the name of the sitcom he starred in as a kid?

Q: *NYPD Blue* was an instant hit and made several actors famous. What was the name of the actor who left after the first season? What was his character's name?

A: 1. B; 2. C; 3. A; 4. D

A: Mel's Diner. The series *Alice* ran from 1976–1985.

A: *Silver Spoons* (1982–1987). He was called "Ricky" back then.

A: David Caruso played John Kelly.

Q: On the late 1970s sitcom *WKRP in Cincinnati*, what famous baseball manager worked for the station for a brief time?

Q: Mr. Spock was from what planet?

Q: What was the name of Bill Cosby's character on *The Cosby Show*? From oldest to youngest, name Bill Cosby's TV children on *The Cosby Show*.

Q: Late in *The Cosby Show* run, Sandra had twins. What were the twins' names?

Q: What planet was Mork from?

A: Sparky Anderson.

A: Vulcan. The original *Star Trek* series ran from 1966–1969.

A: Dr. Heathcliff Huxtable. Sondra, Denise, Theo, Vanessa, and Rudy were his TV kids.

A: Winnie and Nelson, named after Winnie and Nelson Mandela.

A: Ork. The sitcom *Mork and Mindy* ran from 1978–1982 and gave Robin Williams his big start.

Q: Here's a line from a theme song: "Now the world don't move to the beat of just one drum. What might be right for you, may not be right for some." Name the show.

Q: Here's another line from a theme song: "Who can turn the world on with a smile? Who can take a nothing day and suddenly make it all seem worthwhile?" Name the show.

Q: What were the station call letters where Mary Tyler Moore worked on *The Mary Tyler Moore Show*?

Q: In one of the most famous sitcom episodes in TV history, the clown from Mary Tyler Moore's station is killed in a tragic, yet humorous accident. What was this clown's name, and how did he die?

A: *Different Strokes.*

A: *The Mary Tyler Moore Show.*

A: WJM.

A: Chuckles, who was killed by a rogue elephant while dressed as a peanut.

Q: Phyllis on *The Mary Tyler Moore Show*
(1970–1977) was always quick to look down on
Mary. What did Phyllis's husband do to make
her feel so superior?

Q: In the last episode of *The Mary Tyler Moore
Show*, all the characters, save one, are fired from
the station. Which character manages to remain
employed?

Q: What was Perry Como's occupation before he
became famous as a singer and as the host of a
successful musical variety show?

Q: Who was the first African-American to have his
own television show?

A: He was an orthodontist.

A: The bumbling anchorman, Ted Baxter, was the only one to keep his job.

A: Pierino "Perry" Como was called the "Singing Barber." In fact, Como had decided to go back home to Canonsburg, Pennsylvania to open up a barber shop in 1943 when CBS offered him a radio show. By 1948, Como was on television.

A: Nat "King" Cole was the first African-American to have both his own radio show, and later, his own television show. Cole's radio show, which lasted for four years, began in 1946. In October 1956, Nat hosted his own TV show.

Q: What newspaper gossip columnist ended up hosting one of the most popular musical variety television shows of all time?

Q: What British musical act made its American debut on this show in 1964?

Q: What television show made Dick Clark nationally famous?

Q: Who was the host of the *Today* show when it debuted in 1952?

Q: Which future Academy Award winning actress was a "Today Girl" in 1953?

A: Ed Sullivan, who was a Broadway columnist with the New York *Daily News*, hosted a musical variety show every Sunday night for more than two decades (1948–1971). Sullivan had his own unique diction and hand gestures, supplying comics with loads of material.

A: The Beatles. Ed Sullivan featured an incredible variety of entertainment, from Topo Gigio, to Stiller and Meara, to the Beatles.

A: Dick Clark was the host of *American Bandstand*, the first network television show devoted to rock and roll. This Philadelphia-based show had its ABC debut on August 5, 1957 and ran until 1989.

A: Dave Garroway was the host from 1952 to 1961. John Chancellor had a stint in 1961 and 1962, and Hugh Downs took over in 1962, running to 1971.

A: Years before Estelle Parsons won the 1967 Academy Award for Best Supporting Actress for her performance in *Bonnie and Clyde*, she was on *The Today Show*.

Q: What show starred David Janssen as Dr.
Richard Kimble?

Q: What private eye show starred David Janssen?
Who played his secretary Sam?

Q: Who played Marshall Dillon on the western
Gunsmoke? Who played his deputy, Chester
Goode?

Q: The actor who played Marshall Dillon has a
brother who is also an actor. Can you name him?
In which highly rated 1960s show did he star?

Q: Annette Funicello made her television debut on
what afternoon show?

A: *The Fugitive* (1963–1967), whose lead character was a doctor wrongly convicted of murdering his wife, on the run, and searching for the one-armed man he saw running from his house the night of the murder.

A: *Richard Diamond, Private Detective* (1957–1960). Mary Tyler Moore played Sam, but her face is never shown.

A: James Arness was Marshall Matt Dillon in lawless Dodge City on *Gunsmoke* from 1955 to 1975. Dennis Weaver was Chester, the Marshall's deputy, from 1955 to 1964.

A: Peter Graves, born Peter Aurness, played Jim Phelps on the series *Mission Impossible,* from 1967–1973, reprising the role in 1988–1990. James Arness is his older brother.

A: Annette was a Mouseketeer on the original *Mickey Mouse Club* (1955–1959), causing many young hearts to flutter.

Q: What former first baseman for the Brooklyn Dodgers went on to star in his own television western?

Q: When USSR leader Leonid Brezhnev visited the United States in the early 1970s, the White House staff asked him if there were any Americans he would like to meet. What television star did Brezhnev want to meet?

Q: What former Mouseketeer played Jeff Stone on *The Donna Reed Show* (1958–1965)?

Q: One CBS western featured a professional gunfighter who always wore black and lived in the Hotel Carlton in San Francisco. What was the character's name, and what was the name of the show?

A: Chuck Connors played major league baseball in 1949 and 1950 before moving to Hollywood. He was the star (Luke McCain) of ABC's popular western series, *The Rifleman*, which debuted in 1958.

A: Chuck Connors. *The Rifleman* was Breshnev's favorite American show.

A: Paul Peterson played the son of Donna Reed and Carl Betz on *The Donna Reed Show*, a classic family sitcom of the late 1950s. Shelley Fabares played his sister, Mary.

A: Paladin. The name of the show was taken from the motto that appeared on Paladin's business card: *Have Gun—Will Travel*. Richard Boone played Paladin, the gunfighter, in this series that ran from 1957–1963.

Q: Two drama shows about doctors premiered in 1961. What were the names of these two TV doctors?

Q: *Our Miss Brooks* (1952–1956) starred what comedic actress?

Q: What sitcom featured Walter Brennan as Grandpappy Amos?

Q: What actor, later a star on *The Real McCoys*, portrayed a high school student on *Our Miss Brooks*?

Q: What actor played the lead in the television series *The Cisco Kid* (1950–1956)? What was the name of Cisco's sidekick?

A: Vince Edwards starred as Doctor Ben Casey on the show *Ben Casey* (1961–1966), and Richard Chamberlain was Dr. James Kildare on *Dr. Kildare* (1961–1966).

A: Eve Arden was Miss Connie Brooks, an English teacher at Madison High School, run by Principal Osgood Conklin, where she flirts with fellow teacher Mr. Boynton, played by Robert Rockwell.

A: *The Real McCoys* (1957–1963). Grandpappy Amos was the head of the clan. Richard Crenna was Luke McCoy.

A: Richard Crenna made his TV debut as Miss Brooks's adolescent friend Walter Denton.

A: Duncan Renaldo, originally from Romania, played Cisco, who traveled around with Pancho, played by Leo Carrillo. At the end of each program, they would say to each other, "Oh, Cisco!" "Oh, Pancho!"

Q: What were the names of the two lead characters on NBC's *The Man From U.N.C.L.E.* (1964–1968)? What are the names of the actors who played them?

Q: What was the spin-off series of *The Man From U.N.C.L.E.*, that starred Stefanie Powers?

Q: How long did Walter Cronkite do the *CBS Evening News*? How did he end every broadcast?

Q: Who replaced Walter Cronkite on the *CBS Evening News*?

A: International agents Napoleon Solo and Ilya Kuryakin were played by actors Robert Vaughn and David McCullum.

A: *The Girl From U.N.C.L.E.*, which ran for one season in 1966, starred Stefanie Powers as agent April Dancer and Noel Harrison as April's partner Mark Slate.

A: Cronkite was on the *CBS Evening News* from 1962, until his retirement in 1981. He was considered "the most trusted man in America" in a 1960s poll. His nightly sign-off was "And that's the way it is."

A: Fellow Texan Dan Rather.

Q: Who hosted *The Tonight Show* on NBC before Johnny Carson?

Q: What show did Johnny Carson host on daytime television before his stint on *The Tonight Show*?

Q: What innovative comedy show made Goldie Hawn, Arte Johnson, Ruth Buzzi, Lily Tomlin, Joanne Worley, Pigmeat Markham, Gary Owens, Henry Gibson, Judy Crane, and others famous? It also introduced The Flying Fickle Finger of Fate Award.

Q: What future president made an appearance on this show, which was taped in beautiful downtown Burbank?

A: When *The Tonight Show* debuted in 1954, Steve
    Allen was its host. He was followed by Jack Paar in
    1957, and Johnny Carson in 1962, who held the spot
    for nearly thirty years. Jay Leno won the highly
    contested job in 1992.

A: Carson was the host of the ABC quiz show *Who Do
    You Trust?* (1958–1963); it was ABC's highest rated
    daytime program.

A: *Laugh-In* (1968–1973), hosted by Dan Rowan and
    Dick Martin, was the fast-paced NBC comedy show
    that made stars of the talents above.

A: Rowan & Martin's *Laugh-In* even had Richard Nixon
    on, saying "Sock It to Me!"

Q: Two actors co-starred in a series playing Pentagon agents who traveled the world disguised as a tennis player and his trainer. What was the name of the actors and the series?

Q: What was Don Adam's agent number on *Get Smart*? What was the female agent's number?

Q: The actor who played Conrad Siegfried, the nemesis of Maxwell Smart, was also on the 1970s series *Love Boat*, where he played Doctor Adam Bricker. What is this actor's name?

Q: What was Hawkeye and Trapper's (later Hawkeye and B.J.'s) tent affectionately called on *M*A*S*H* (1972–1983)?

A: Robert Culp played tennis star Kelly Robinson, and Bill Cosby played his trainer, Alexander Scott, in the series *I Spy* (1965-1968).

A: Agent 86. Barbara Feldon was 99. The two agents married late in the show's run.

A: Bernie Kopell.

A: The Swamp.

Q: On *M*A*S*H*, what was Klinger's favorite baseball team?

Q: Another *M*A*S*H* question: What was Hawkeye's rank?

Q: Who played Mrs. Peel on the British-made ABC show, *The Avengers?*

Q: What town was Jessica Fletcher's home in *Murder, She Wrote?*

Q: Early in their careers, Don Knotts, Louis Nye, and Tom Poston played "men on the street" on what Sunday evening show?

A: The Toledo Mudhens.

A: Captain.

A: Diana Rigg was Mrs. Peel from 1965 to 1967, playing alongside Patrick Macnee as John Steed. When she left the show, Linda Thorson replaced her, but, as competent as she was, it wasn't the same.

A: Angela Lansbury, as mystery writer Jessica Fletcher, lived in Cabot Cove, Maine. It seemed like Cabot Cove must have had the highest murder rate in the United States for the years from 1984–1996.

A: *The Steve Allen Show* (1956–1960). One of the regular features of the show was Steve's "Man on the street"—Don Knotts as the nervous interviewee, Tom Poston as the man who could not remember, and Louis Nye as Gordon Hathaway ("Hi, Ho, Steverino").

Q: What was the name of the town where Andy Griffith was the sheriff?

Q: What popular sitcom of the 1960s was a spin-off of the *Andy Griffith Show*?

Q: What book publisher was a regular panelist on the weekly show, *What's My Line* (1950–1967)?

Q: What matinee idol movie star was a police sergeant on *McMillan and Wife*?

Q: *Car 54, Where Are You*? Where was Car 54, anyway?

A: Mayberry, North Carolina. Sheriff Andy Taylor and his son Opie live with Aunt Bea. Andy's deputy is Barney Fife, played by Don Knotts.

A: *Gomer Pyle USMC* (1964–1970). Jim Nabors played Gomer Pyle, a bumbling Marine from Mayberry, who was stationed far away from home at Camp Henderson.

A: Along with Arlene Francis and Dorothy Kilgalllen, Bennett Cerf, publisher of Random House books, was a panelist trying to guess the occupations of guests by asking "yes or no" questions. John Daly was the moderator.

A: Rock Hudson starred in this series in the 1970s. His wife was played by Susan Saint James.

A: Fred Gwynne and Joe E. Ross, as officers Muldoon and Toody, created havoc as cops in the Bronx (1961–1963).

Q: What was the name of the lead character on *The Phil Silvers Show (You'll Never Get Rich)?*

Q: What was an unusual plot device that George Burns employed on the 1950s *The George Burns & Gracie Allen Show?*

Q: What was the name of the D.A. who lost every week to Perry Mason?

Q: Who were the hosts of the CBS *Children's Film Festival* (1947–1957)?

Q: What 1950s sitcom revolved around a nightclub singer, who had a wife and three children, and a relative named Uncle Tonoose?

A: Phil Silvers was Sgt. Bilko, the con man who ran the motor pool at Fort Baxter.

A: George was often seen in his den, watching and commenting on the program we were watching.

A: Running from September 1957 until May 1966, D.A. Hamilton Burger, played by William Talman, was the prosecutor who lost every week on *Perry Mason*.

A: Kukla, Fran, and Ollie were the hosts. Fran Allison was the woman, and Kukla the Clown and Ollie the Alligator were puppets. Burr Tillstrom was the puppeteer.

A: *Make Room for Daddy*, also called *The Danny Thomas Show*.

Q: What host of the comedy-variety television show, *The Texaco Star Theater* (1948–1953), was known as "Mr. Television"?

Q: Who occupied the center square on *Hollywood Squares* in the 1970s?

Q: One top-rated show from the 1950s featured the Anderson family, with Jim Anderson, an insurance agent, dispensing advice to his wife, two daughters, and a son named Bud. What was its name?

Q: Eddie Haskell ("that's a nice dress you have on, Mrs. Cleaver") was a character on what 1950s sitcom?

A: Milton Berle was the host of TV's first big hit show—a show that was so popular that it is said that it spurred sales of television sets.

A: Paul Lynde became a regular in the fall of 1968, and was moved into the vital center square spot. Lynde was paid much more than the other celebrities on the show. These days, Whoopi Goldberg occupies the center square.

A: *Father Knows Best*, starring Robert Young and Jane Wyatt as the parents, and Eleanor Donahue (Betty), Billy Gray (Bud), and Lauren Chapin (Kathy) as the children.

A: *Leave It to Beaver.* The show revolved around "the Beaver," who lived with his parents, Ward and June, and his older brother Wally. Eddie Haskell was the ingratiating neighbor.

Q: Clem Kaddiddlehopper was a character on what long-running TV show?

Q: What actor played Judge Bradley Stevens on *I Married Joan* and was the voice of the cartoon character Mr. Magoo?

Q: Who played Charlie and Doris Hickenlooper in skits on *Your Show of Shows*?

Q: What was the name of the narrator of the 1960s series *The Twilight Zone*?

A: Clem was just one of the funny characters played by Red Skelton on *The Red Skelton Show*, which ran from 1951 to 1971.

A: Jim Backus was on the 1950s sitcom with Joan Davis as his wife, Joan Stevens. He was also the voice of Mr. Magoo, and played Thurston Howell III on *Gilligan's Island*.

A: Sid Caesar and Imogene Coca were the couple on the live 90-minute show, which ran every Saturday night on NBC from February 1950 to June 1954.

A: Writer and creator Rod Serling introduced every program of this weekly series.

Q: What 1950s comedy show starred a 39 year old comic, and featured the cast of Eddie "Rochester" Anderson, Mary Livingtone, Frank Nelson, Don Wilson, Dennis Day, and even Mel Blanc?

Q: What future president hosted *Death Valley Days*?

Q: Who played Corporal Peter Newkirk on *Hogan's Heroes* (1965–1971)?

Q: What game show did this actor later host?

A: *The Jack Benny Show.*

A: Ronald Reagan was the host of *Death Valley Days* for a few years in the 1960s, but he survived Death Valley, and went on to be Governor of California, and President of the United States.

A: Richard Dawson.

A: Dawson puckered up as the host of *Family Feud* from 1976–1984.

Q: What late 1970s show featured a free-wheeling truck driver and his best friend, who just happened to be a monkey?

Q: What was the first name of Aunt Esther's husband on the 1970s show *Sanford & Son*?

Q: What studio does NBC's *Saturday Night Live* air from?

Q: Can you name all of the "Weekend Update" anchors from *Saturday Night Live* up through the 2000–2001 season?

A: *BJ and the Bear*. Bear was the monkey, in case you were wondering. BJ was played by Greg Evigan.

A: Willie.

A: Studio 8-H, in New York City.

A: Chevy Chase (1975–1976), Jane Curtin (1976–1980), Dan Aykroyd (1977–1978), Bill Murray (1978–1980), Charles Rocket (1980–1981), Gail Matthius (1981), Brian Doyle-Murray (1981–1982), Mary Gross (1981–1982), Christine Ebersole (1982), Brad Hall (1982–1984), Christopher Guest (1984–1985), Dennis Miller (1985–1991), Kevin Nealon (1991–1994), Norm Macdonald (1994–1997), Colin Quinn (1998–2000), and Jimmy Fallon and Tina Fey (2000–2001).

Q: What did Wonder Woman's golden lasso do to criminals?

Q: Who was the original host of the 1980s music and dance show *Solid Gold*?

Q: What business were Eliot and Michael of *thirtysomething* in?

Q: Who narrated *The Wonder Years* (1988–1993)?

Q: Where did the Munsters live?

A: When wrapped around the bad guy, it forced them to tell the truth. *Wonder Woman* ran from 1976 to 1979, and starred Lynda Carter.

A: Dionne Warwick.

A: Advertising.

A: The voice of Kevin in his later years was supplied by Daniel Stern.

A: The creepy 1960s family lived at 1313 Mockingbird Lane.

Q: What language did Morticia speak that drove Gomez crazy on *The Addams Family*?

Q: What kind of car did the 1970s policemen Starsky & Hutch drive?

Q: With what song did Donny and Marie open their 1970s variety show?

Q: Name the actors who played the two Darrins on *Bewitched*.

Q: What costume problem did Barbara Eden have to deal with on the 1960s show *I Dream of Jeannie*?

Q: What TV show launched the career of movie star Bruce Willis?

A: French.

A: A 1974 Ford Torino.

A: "I'm a little bit country, and I'm a little bit rock and roll." Marie was the "country," so that left Donny as the "rock and roll."

A: Dick York was on the show from 1964–1969, and Dick Sargent was Darrin from 1969–1972.

A: Because of NBC's "No Navel" edict, she was not allowed to show her belly button.

A: Bruce played private detective David Addison in *Moonlighting* (1985–1989), which co-starred Cybill Shepherd as Maddie Hayes.

Q: According to the voice-over in the beginning of the *Odd Couple* (1971–1975), on what date was Felix Unger asked by his wife to remove himself from his place of residence?

Q: What ground-breaking TV series of the 1990s was originally called *These Friends of Mine*?

Q: What were names of the two lead officers in the late 1970s show *CHiPs*?

Q: What kind of pet did the fashionable vice cop Sonny Crockett keep on his boat?

Q: What musical TV series of the 1970s made a teen idol out of David Cassidy?

A: November 13th.

A: *Ellen,* starring Ellen DeGeneres. The show was re-titled after the first season.

A: Jon and Ponch kept the Los Angeles Freeways safe. Jon was played by Larry Wilcox, Ponch by Erik Estrada. Wilcox left before the last season, and was replaced by Tom Reilly (as Bobby "Hot Dog" Nelson) who in turn was replaced by Bruce Penhall (as Bruce Nelson, Bobby's younger brother).

A: On the 1980s series *Miami Vice,* Sonny kept an alligator named Elvis.

A: *The Partridge Family.*

Q: What boy detective TV series of the 1970s made a teen idol out of Sean Cassidy?

Q: What affliction does Mary Ingalls struggle with, as a result of her bout with scarlet fever?

Q: What show revolved around the question, "Who killed Laura Palmer?"

Q: Who played the scheming stow-away Dr. Smith on *Lost in Space*?

Q: What was very unusual about the cousins Cathy and Patty Lane on the *Patty Duke Show*?

Q: Before Tony Danza appeared on *Who's the Boss?* (1984–1990), what other popular series was he on?

A: *The Hardy Boys.*

A: The eldest daughter on *Little House on the Prairie* (1974–1984) went blind after her illness.

A: David Lynch's surreal *Twin Peaks* (1990–1991). In case you missed it, Laura was killed by her father Leland, who was possessed by an evil spirit named Bob.

A: Jonathan Harris. The sci-fi series ran from 1965 to 1968.

A: They were identical cousins. Patty Duke played both roles in this 1960s series.

A: Tony Danza played Tony Banta on *Taxi* (1978–1983), a sitcom set in a New York City taxi garage. This series also starred Danny DeVito, Judd Hirsch, Marilu Henner, Andy Kaufman, and Carol Kane.

Q: Who was Latka's smarmy lounge lizard alter-ego on *Taxi*?

Q: What is the favorite hangout of the cabbies on *Taxi* called?

Q: Who directed the first regular series episode of *Columbo* in 1971?

Q: Warren Beatty appeared as a regular in what popular fifties sitcom?

Q: What future sitcom star had a short-lived role on the 1980s TV show *Benson*?

Q: Before becoming a movie megastar, Jim Carrey had a part on what TV show?

A: Vic Ferrari. Andy Kaufman brought both characters to life on this series.

A: Mario's. "Reverend" Jim eventually buys the place.

A: Steven Spielberg.

A: In the 1959–1960 season of *The Many Loves of Dobie Gillis*, Beatty played Milton Armitage.

A: Jerry Seinfeld played Frankie on *Benson*, which starred Robert Guillaume as the title character.

A: *In Living Color* (1990–1994), which starred Keenen Ivory Wayans.

Q: What was the name of "the love boat"?

Q: What was the name of the fort where F-Troop was stationed?

Q: Who won a million dollars as the first champion of the reality show *Survivor*?

Q: Bob Newhart was the star of two very popular sitcoms, one in the 1970s and one in the 1980s. Fittingly, the first was called *The Bob Newhart Show* and the second was called *Newhart*. What did the buttoned-down Newhart do for a living on each show?

Q: Who played Bob Newhart's wives on *The Bob Newhart Show* and *Newhart*?

A: The amorous ship was the *Pacific Princess*.

A: Fort Courage—the wacky 1960s sitcom starred Forrest Tucker, Ken Berry, and Larry Storch.

A: Richard Hatch.

A: He was a psychiatrist on *The Bob Newhart Show,* and he owned an inn on *Newhart*.

A: Suzanne Plechette played wife number one (Emily Hartley), and Mary Frann played wife number two (Joanna Loudon).

Q: He was at one time a famed member of the E Street Band. Now he can be seen as a mafioso on *The Sopranos*. Who is this rocker turned actor?

Q: Lorraine Braco plays Dr. Melfi, Tony Sprano's psychiatrist, on *The Sopranos*. In what movie did she play the wife of a gangster?

Q: What is the name of the strip club where Tony Soprano and his buddies hang out?

Q: The characters on *Just Shoot Me* work at a fashion magazine. What is the name of the magazine?

Q: Karen on *Will & Grace* has a real love/hate relationship with her housekeeper. What is the name of the housekeeper?

A: Steve Van Zandt plays Silvio on *The Sopranos*.

A: Lorraine Braco was nominated for a Best Supporting Actress Oscar for her role in *Goodfellas*.

A: Bada Bing.

A: *Blush*.

A: Rosario, played by Shelly Morrison.

Q: Name the actor who plays President Josiah Bartlett on *The West Wing*.

Q: What star of the movie *Grease* plays President Bartlett's wife?

Q: On the *X-Files*, William B. Davis played an unnamed man with a bad habit—what did Agents Scully and Mulder call his character?

Q: Name the only current *60 Minutes* correspondent who has been with the show since its inception in 1968.

A: Martin Sheen.

A: *The West Wing*'s First Lady is played by Stockard Channing, who starred as Rizzo in the movie *Grease*.

A: The Cigarette Smoking Man. Gillian Anderson plays Agent Scully, and Fox Mulder was played by David Duchovnoy, who left the show in 2001.

A: Mike Wallace.